GILES

DAILY✠EXPRESS AND **SUNDAY✠EXPRESS**

CARTOONS

FIFTY FIFTH SERIES

GILES CHARACTERS™ & © 2001 Express Newspapers

Published by

Pedigree®

The Old Rectory, Matford Lane, Exeter, Devon, EX2 4PS
email: books@pedigreegroup.co.uk
Under licence from Express Newspapers
ISBN 1-902836-63-4

Gl 55

An Introduction by

Sir Trevor McDonald OBE

I am delighted to have been asked to contribute this foreword to the commemorative Annual of Carl Giles' work. I became a fan when I was relatively young and living in Trinidad in the West Indies. Under the influence of my father who had little time for reading too many books, we were encouraged as a family to join in the fun of looking at Giles cartoons because they brilliantly encapsulated almost every aspect of life and with great wit, verve, bite and humour.

I remember coming to the view that people in England had the wonderful ability to laugh at themselves. I regard that as a great asset and a virtue in an otherwise naughty and sometimes appalling world. For me Giles' cartoons have another special element. They are funny but unfailingly good-natured. They make you laugh out loud, but you are never made to feel uneasy about the spite or vindictiveness that inhabit so much of what passes for humour today.

Giles bravely spoke out for those who might never have otherwise had a voice of their own. He held up to delicious ridicule those who in assuming positions of responsibility in our society, confuse that with self-importance. He punctured pomposity and he clearly hated injustices. I have always enjoyed that about his work most of all. His cartoons speak to us in their extraordinary variety as the voice of real genius.

Sir Trevor McDonald, OBE

"I suppose some top-hatted official will get the credit for this extra half pint of milk today."

"Equal rights? You've got equal rights; you're in our Victory Parade, aren't you?"

"So - I bring him to see the sea for the first time and he says he'd sooner see a good air raid any day."

"I see we can get sports equipment without a permit now - all except cricket gear and 'ockey balls."

"Well - there go your old girl friends."

"Poor John - someone's written and blamed him for not feeding our racehorses as well as the French."
John Strachey, Minister of Food, (1946 - 1950).

"Cheer up, girls - you'll soon get into the swing of cussing the new one."

"Ferdi, beer being the price it is since the Budget, I know you will appreciate how anxious we are that you get well very, very quickly."

'Which of you is called Percy?'

Unfortunately, Tom, they can't eat money.

"Boy! You sure hypnotised this one. Third day since kick-off, and he ain't woke up yet."

"Now we'll try it this way - Rank can take over Transport, Strachey take over films, and Alf Barnes can take over Strachey's groundnuts."

"I'm shortly attending a meeting of Fleet-street journalists - these are my measurements. . ."

"Then, when you've had enough of housewives chivvying you around,
come out here and have a basin of groundnuts."

"Quit telling Mr. Strachey to mind his nut. Mr. Strachey's very touchy about nuts."

"You can't expect a fire in your waiting-room - AND in the engine."

"Nationalised corned beef-eaters - that's what we are."

"Probably M.P.s."

"They'll want to send Cambridge an American admiral now . . ."

"In view of the splendid example set by Cabinet Ministers this week I'd like you to knock my salary in 'arf."

"Such unfair distribution of Home Guards will enable the Eastern Counties to invade our Western Counties any time they feel like it."

"Once more unto the breach, dear friends, once more . . ."

"Gertrude, my sweet, it seems I am not the only one who ignores his loved one's advice about a balanced diet."

VOTE FOR A GOOD-LOOKING PARTY?

"They did something letting little princes blow whistles to start trains."

"Mon petit Anglais! We remember you well when here you was in the war! You must stay to dîner."

"Whatever you do, don't let her know the Mounties haven't 'got their man' on a horse for years."

"That's all for tonight, Miss - you can let him go now."

"Oh yeah, yeah, yeah?"

"PSST! Are you interested in advertising?"

"At least he's given the boys a bit of incentive."

REPORTING . . AN INCIDENT DURING THE GILES FAMILY'S PROGRESS ALONG THE ROAD TO THE HIGHLANDS

"What are you giving 'em today - bayonet practice or Bebop?"

"How does he do it? Signs himself 'Eddie Calvert,' that's how he does it."

"Fellows, I have information for thee - Chalky is going to collect your National Savings after all."

"We've got a smashing big car coming tomorrow, Mum - a pretty lady at the show talked Dad into it."

"Honey, can't you simply resign from the Party and leave it at that?"

"If Ike <u>had</u> sent U.S. soldiers to shoot Israelis Mr. Ben Hecht with his song in his heart would have looked a bit of a twerp."

"I wonder how the Joneses fared with their travel allowance in Moscow, my love?"

"I don't think Lord Altrincham would go a lot on Nobby's delivery of speech about Lord Londonderry."
(With apologies for using the pictorial beauty of some of the transport drivers I met in Lancashire last week.)

"We are going to let Stirling Moss have a handful for his wedding every time he came round."

"Not the least objection to women in the House of Lords is arriving at one's club reeking like an infernal beauty parlour."

"I would be a happy man if Tessa and Dominic, Belinda Lee, and Diana Dors would emigrate to the Pole 'wearing their best publicity briefs.'"
This extract from a reader's letter published last week caused mixed opinions among husbands and wives in residence at the Pole.

"Now why don't you two young gentlemen get on your allotment and give Mr. Krushchev a day off?"

"The Lord's Day Observance Society do not approve of ballet on Sundays. I fear they would not go a lot on 'Rock-a-boogie-houn'-dog' either."

"I think the Avenue has done very well in the Honours List - two Knights and one
Order of the British Empire."

"Men, the entertainments committee have suggested we invite Terry Dene to entertain us at a camp party."
Terry Dene, Britain's "Elvis" inducted into army in 1959.

"Thanks to your doggy friends in the House of Lords you and me are taking a damn silly walk in the park instead of watching TV by a nice warm fire."

"Don't blame the German people - it's only the irresponsible few."

"No dispute about <u>that</u> one being a 'throw', Harry."

"Here we are - more and more people find enjoyment afloat, adventure or relaxation, excitement or away-from-it-all peace."

"As far as I can make with the interpreter they're congratulating us on Kennedy's escape from America."

"News for thee, Comrades."

"The Court will most certainly NOT allow costs for the defendant's broken umbrella."

"I don't care if we are as good as in the Common Market - until we are, mate <u>we</u> still changa da guard at Buckingham Palace."

"Since they've cut his subsidies economy's gone to his head."

"When Mr. Marples asked motorists to travel by moonlight I'm sure he didn't mean instead of headlights."

"If four Beatles disguised as coppers equals one helmet each how come we've got 23 souvenirs?"

"How d'you like commercial TV's St. George's Day answer to B.B.C.2 and B.B.C.1's week of Shakespeare?"

"Mr. Jordan isn't going to like us reporting that one of his stormtroopers' wives won't let him come out to throw little bags of flour at meetings."

"Well, there's one who doesn't entirely sympathise with Rodney's witty quips about
Jo Grimmond having Wilson and Heath by the ears."

"You wouldn't be wishing to be the only visitor leaving Dublin without a genuine head of Nelson himself."

"That's Mummy for you - Hailsham Hogg says they'll lynch the Labour Party if they get in, so away we go knitting hangmen's ropes."

"The Leader says to stop savaging phone boxes - we want 'em for making daft calls to No.10."

"Bang - how about that? In her day a couple of gunboats would have stopped this Mao keeping us out of the Common Market."

"Why are we booking you if we didn't book him? Because <u>he</u> wasn't playing polo on a bike in the middle of a motorway, for one reason."

"On your feet, Sir Francis - we've won ten years' free mooring in the Daily Express Boat Show competition."

"Ivan, did you tell this lady who called for her cat if she didn't push off she'd get six years in the salt mines?"

"Is that Sir Basil Smallpiece? Can we lend you our independent expert on the Concorde to check your diagnosis on the Q.E.2?"

"Like it says, dear - the Cooper-Tomasoni fight will be broadcast live on TV tonight."

"Achtung! You are about to be helped to get rid of your Deutschmarks."

"It's about time you taught that wee bull of yours the difference between the Government and the Opposition."

INDUSTRIAL WAR DANCE
Description by Transport Workers' Union leader of the Employment Minister's speech

"Not only does the union disapprove of begging, Miss, but we understand that you have just acquired the latest Paris outfit by Cardin."

"Philip, did you telephone the council about this new rent assistance bill?"

"These 'ere Editors of OZ have had a remarkable influence on some of the regulars."

"Scotland Yard are sending us a Detective Chief Inspector Barlow. They must be joking, I hope."

"It's a trap! 'Get on board and picket them Tall ships', was our orders."

"That's your Pa - anything rather than accept free dole from the British, or a lift home from Wimpy's."

"Of course we are all very happy they are re-united, but we think a thanksgiving service in St. Peter's is coming it a bit much."

"If I had the choice of spending the week in Canada and rushing back to get on a boat I know which I'd choose."

"Very well, Prime Minister - we'll see you round here about four p.m. then we'll all be able to explain your Phase 3 to you."

"Goodness, no trains? Whatever's been going on during my Christmas recess?"

"Honestly Ref, I only meant to belt him one - I didn't mean to exorcise him."

"I brought my smile to work and all I got was: 'What the hell are you grinning at?'"

"Mr. Wilson would know all about Rough Justice if he knocked Grandma's Guiness over and I got one because I was the nearest"

"Mrs Thatcher preaching in America says: 'Opportunity, if it means anything, must be an opportunity to be unequal.'"

"'Tis Ladies' Day, Harry."

"Relax, they're mine."

"WAKEY, WAKEY! D-DAY!"

"We've got a refund hunter expecting the extra 5$\frac{1}{2}$p a gallon to be scrapped tomorrow"

"Unlike other Judges in the news, young lady, I am not prepared to overlook your misdemeanours to benefit your promising career"

"With my wife, her mother, our local sergeant and your guard-dog, I feel we might proceed in an atmosphere of maximum security, Mrs. Wimpole."

"I'll decide when we apply sanctions to Ford owners - go serve the customer."

"A white puff means Enoch Powell is talking through his hat, a black puff means their oil heater needs a new burner."

"In view of what happened at Wimbledon this week - and for the honour of the Club - have a care Mrs. Wintergreen."

"Mark - some gentlemen from Leyland to have a word with you about closed shop"

"'As all HRH's heart-throbs are backing him to win, let's grease his saddle so he falls off?' What a wicked thought Fred!"

"I'm not changing my name to Mrs. Bonio Smirnoff-Bovril to get sponsors for you to go to the Olympics."

"Funny - nothing in the papers about this blasted fellah, Benn"

"Listen, sonny boy - the one on your right belongs to H.R.H., the one on your left is mine."

"Smuggling booze into the game in an empty after-shave lotion bottle wasn't very canny, Angus"

"What do they call 'em for fraternising with the enemy? Ruddy fifth columnists"

"Let me explain the World Monetary decline and the repercussions of the Healey-Benn election results, my dear"

"Deporting burglars to England for life will go a long way to helping crime prevention."

"Ignore anything you've read about what Mr. Boycott said of coloured people when he was in India."

"The Avenue-Get-You-To-Work-Coach is here - they're leaving early."

"It's from Maggie - she's going to sue if she doesn't get in."

"There's a couple of cops mucking about in our pool"

"I understand from a council survey that by prostituting your services on TV advertising, you earn more per baked bean than I earn in a year."

"You can't hide here for long, Sir Geoffrey. She'll get you sooner or later now she's back."

"I'll be glad when these TV sessions of donkeys drinking Guinness for Mr Reagan are over."

"Did Matilda watch Science of Sexual Attraction on TV last night, Mr Harris?"

"Harry, how many fingers do we use to salute a General - I forget."

"Permission to land, please"

"We suggest we avoid jokes about him qualifying for cheap bus fares and half price at the cinema now he's 65."

"We certainly will not call in Bob Geldof for advice on how to feed him."

"Gentleman at the back - with libel costs at £500,000 a go, please be careful!"

"Only one thing will keep this off the front page - if your wife came in with the Chancellor of the Exchequer"

"One couldn't tell Emlyn Hughes on TV to do the same as I told the cameraman on the train."

"Yaroo, chaps! Gatting has gone home with the stumps and the Umpire has gone off with the ball"

"Tell that woman the court is only concerned where the defendant was on the night of the crime, not what he thinks of Fergie's latest hat."

"Your MP asks was your attack provoked by the new Social Security changes or Mr Tebbit's attack on your Bonnie Prince Charlie?"

"I've enough on my mind with Tebbit without hopping up and down getting your damn security guard glasses of water."

"However much you support Margaret's principles I think it is a mistake to publicise them, Rosemary."

"Remember last time a newspaper sent some stolen love letters back unopened? You didn't open them either."

"The Judge didn't let me off because I've got a baby - but I get time off for his good behaviour"

"Thanks to Judge Pickles the cleaners are putting in for a 10 per cent rise - it takes longer to clean up after a dinosaur than a judge."

"Dad handed in his war medals in protest against the Poll Tax"

"I expect you will be getting your papers to rejoin the Bengal Lancers any day now, Colonel."

Reynolds News

7 January 1940

"'Morning, wiseguys. Have you heard anything of the
Graf Spec lately?"

"Would you mind giving us a lift?"

"Alack! There lies more peril in thine eye than twenty of their swords." - Romeo and Juliet.

'And What's Our Little Man Found Now?'

'I Hope You Gentlemen Aren't Going To Cheat *This* Time'

"I feel, therefore, that I am compelled to hand
in my resignation."

'How many times 'ave I told you not to
mention apple-sauce!!'

21 April 1940

"Tch! Tch! - There She Goes Again!"

19 May 1940

"A pity der vind it changed, Mein Reverence."

"I tell you we ain't interested in electric heaters."

"I like this bit, Musso. They refer to you here as 'this five-foot-six' waddling tin-pan Caesar.'"

"O.K., Buddies. Reach for the ceiling. This is a stick-up."

"All I said to the sergeant was: 'What couldn't you do to a nice pint?' "

"When you can spare a minute, Boss, there's someone here to see you"

"At a wild guess, Herr Gomm, I should say we are arriving at Whipsnade."

13 October 1940

"I suppose you wouldn't like a wash, polish and grease
while you're here?"

20 October 1940

"And that about makes us quits for that darn
great hole in my garden."

"His Lordship's remarks should be quite interesting when he sees this little lot, Cooper."

"And now we'll ask Mr. Murphy to play the third movement of Brahims' Concerto No. 3 in B Flat Major, Opus 83."

"Suppose we pull this lot up for speeding?"

"Gentlemen - when this war is over we must see that it is absolutely impossible for there to be any danger of another peace."

"I said I bet you'd op if I took this lot over your foot."

Dear Mum - I am now a prisoner of war. The people here do all they can to make us feel at home, the guards are very kind to us and the food is simply marvellous . . .

"Rimmel! They toss der coin for vich vun gif us der vorks!"

"WHY'S 'E GOT MORE THAN ME?"

"Well, how's things in Arcadia?"

"At least he doesn't have a ————— sergeant bawling at him all day long."

"And when you come to think that Hitler reckons the Germans are the superior race——."

"And where would you be if parliament 'adn't passed the Declaration of Rights in 1689?"

"'E was Beethoven yesterday so I'm goin' to be Beethoven to-day."

"So you sent your luggage in advance. Private Abercromby?"

"I've asked him. He says he ain't."

"Queer sort of cove. Every time he passes he says: 'Well, well, well. Only a few days for Christmas'."

11 January 1942

25 January 1942

"Corporal - Take these things out of here!"

"This is nothing, Tovarishi. You should have seen the one that got away."

"I assure you that I feel no desire what ever to indulge in your primitive horse-play."

"Dammit, Sir! You're another of those confounded Reds!"

"Don't let this fancy Cossack stuff get you down. I've seen it all before in circuses."

"Weddin'? I ain't 'eard nothin' about no weddin'"

29 March 1942

"I'm afraid you're going to find me a rather difficult person to jog along with, and perhaps a little intolerant, Sergeant-Major."

12 April 1942

"I want you men to imagine the enemy are approaching in large numbers, supported by tanks, flamethrowers, paratroops, etc., etc. . ."

"Did I understand you to say you've killed me?"

"Trust Sahibs please to excuse violation of honourable game."

31 May 1942

14 June 1942

"O.K. Sunshine. Drop Ace on 'is Queen and 'op outside."

"Don't it make you wish you was one of them real soldiers, Fred?"

"Don't be selfish, Ivan. This one is for our little Anna."

"I've got spurs that jingle jangle jingle . . ."

Young Ernie by *Giles*

1 November 1942

8 November 1942

22 November 1942

29 November 1942

15 December 1942

27 December 1942

20 December 1942

10 January 1943

17 January 1943

7 February 1943

31 January 1943

4 April 1943